HEINEMANN MATHEMATICS 1

Name

WORKBOOK 4

Number to 10 : Relationships

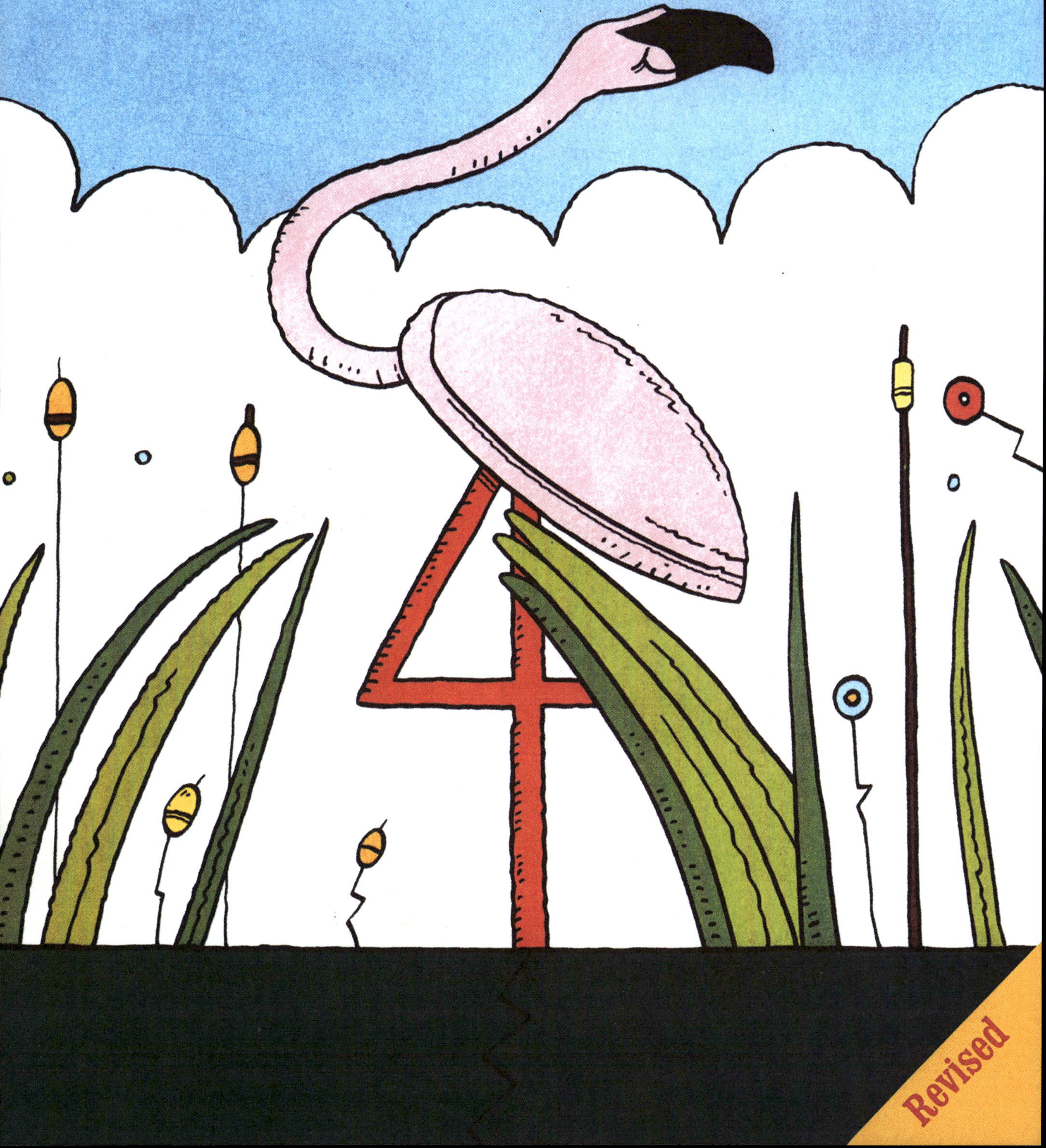

Revised

How much?

Bus tickets

Jan has ☐ p

Can she buy [Bus ticket **7** p] ? ☐ Yes or no?

Sam has ☐ p

Can he buy [Bus ticket **8** p] ? ☐

Jess has ☐ p

Can she buy [Bus ticket **10** p] ? ☐

3

Join the dots.

1 to 10

Bees

1 2 3 4 5 6 7 8 9 10

Write the number

after 3

after 6

after 9

after 5

before 2

before 8

Flower garden

Ring the one that is different.

On the

| 1 one | 2 two | 3 three | 4 four | 5 five |

beach

| 6 six | 7 seven | 8 eight | 9 nine | 10 ten |

How many?

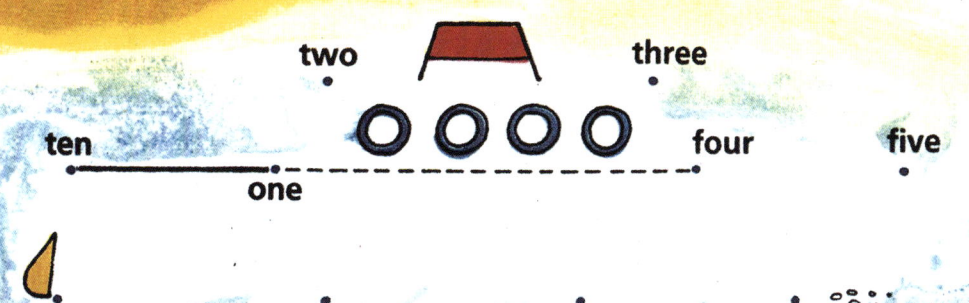

two • three •

ten • one four • five •

nine • eight • seven • six •

Cooks

2 two

eight

four

ten

six

three

one

five

nine

seven

ten ⌒ one

seven

nine

• two

eight

six •

• three

five •

• four

Colour the first red, the second blue, and the third green.

Match

has a

Sam

Pam

Ali

Colour the clothes

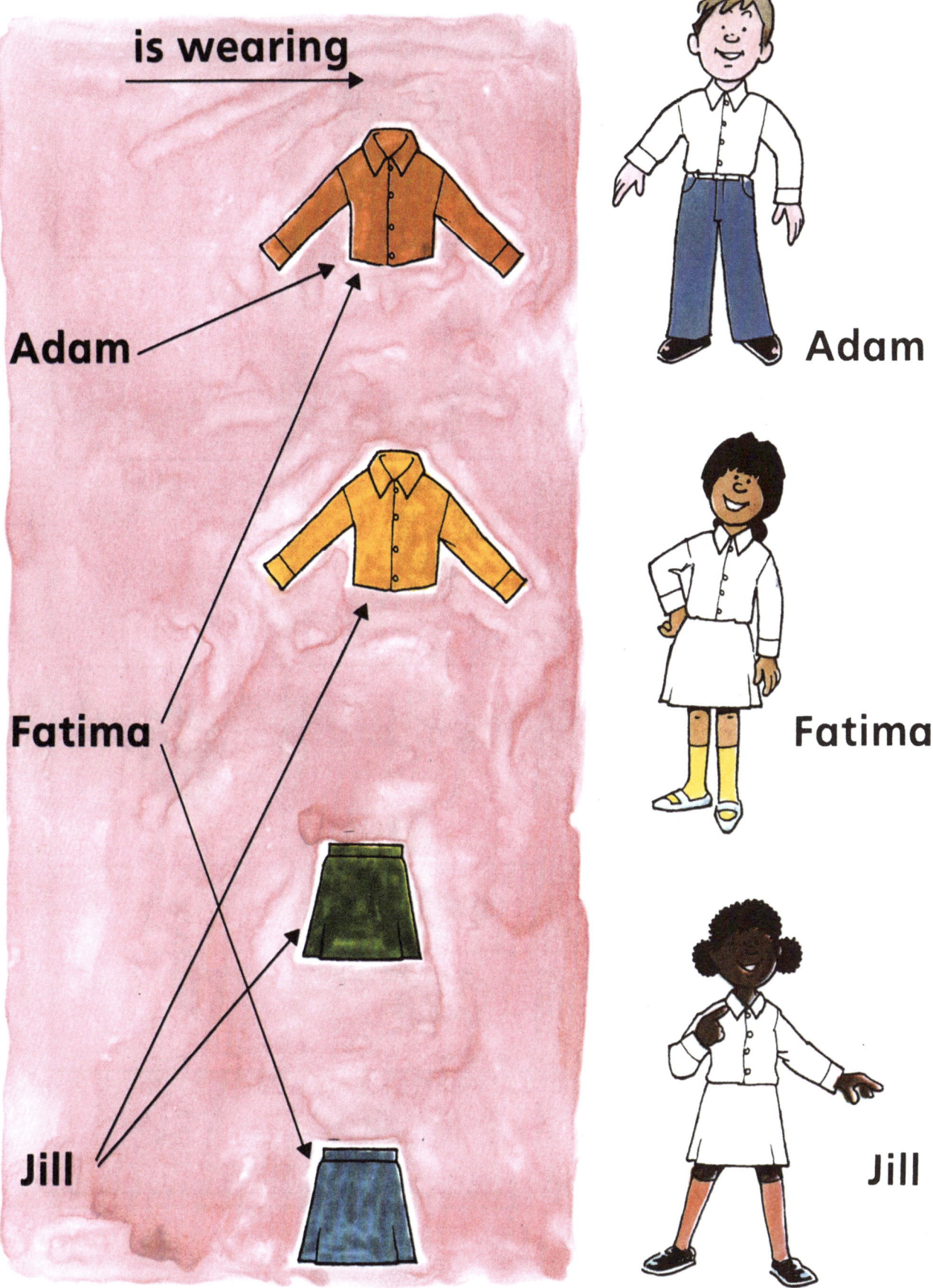

Our group

How many

girls [ ]

boys [ ] ?

Draw one more boy.

How many boys now?

[ ]

girls   boys

Spots

How many?

black spots | 2 |

blue spots | |

red spots | |

Draw my **blue** spots and my **red** spots.

black   **blue**   **red**

1p coins

| 5p | 🍎 | 🍊 | 7p | 🍌 | 4p |

Colour 1p coins to buy.

1	2	3	4	5	6	7	8	9	10	11	12	13	14	15

Heinemann is an imprint of Pearson Education Limited, a company incorporated in England and Wales, having its registered office at Edinburgh Gate, Harlow, Essex, CM20 2JE.
Registered company number: 872828
ISBN 978 0 435 03085 8 © Scottish Primary Mathematics Group 1991.
First published 1991. Revised edition 1995.   22   30
Typeset and illustrated by Oxprint Design.